JOURNAL29

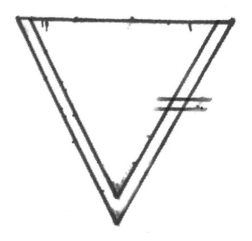

INTERACTIVE BOOK GAME

Journal 29 is a book game of riddles and puzzles.

You will need:
- A copy of Journal 29,
- A pencil
- An internet connected device (preferably a smartphone)

Every two pages of Journal 29 have two elements:
The riddle page and the key page.

Step1:
Solve the riddle on the riddle page.

Step2:
Visit the URL from the key page
*(You can type the URL on your browser
or scan the unique QR code
available on the page.)*

Step3:
Submit the answer of the riddle.
(Answer correctly and get a key, usually a word.)

Step4:
Write down the key.
(These keys are needed for solving the next riddles.)

In the next pages replace the {Key.xx} with the keys you collect

To solve the riddles you will need to think out of the box.
Write, draw, search, fold pages, combine and more.
You don't need any special app to play the game.
Just a browser will do

Turn page to play a demo riddle >

STEP 2
VISIT THIS URL
OR SCAN THE QR CODE:

Journal29.com/0

Scan or visit
the url above
to answer and
collect the key

STEP 3
ANSWER CORRECTLY
AND WRITE DOWN
THE KEY:

key.0: ___START___

STEP 1
THIS IS THE RIDDLE/PUZZLE PAGE
SOLVE THIS:

25+4

A TOP SECRET EXCAVATION DID NOT
BRING ANY RESULT FOR 28 WEEKS.
IT WAS ON THE 29TH WEEK THAT
SOMETHING UNEXPECTED HAPPENED.
THE TEAM DISAPPEARED AND THE
ONLY THING THAT WAS LEFT BEHIND
WAS THIS JOURNAL.

Journal29.com/1

Scan or visit
the url above
to answer and
collect the key

key.1: _____

What a better way to start a new week?

Journal29.com/2

Scan or visit
the url above
to answer and
collect the key

key.2: _____

Journal29.com/3

Scan or visit
the url above
to answer and
collect the key

key.3: _____

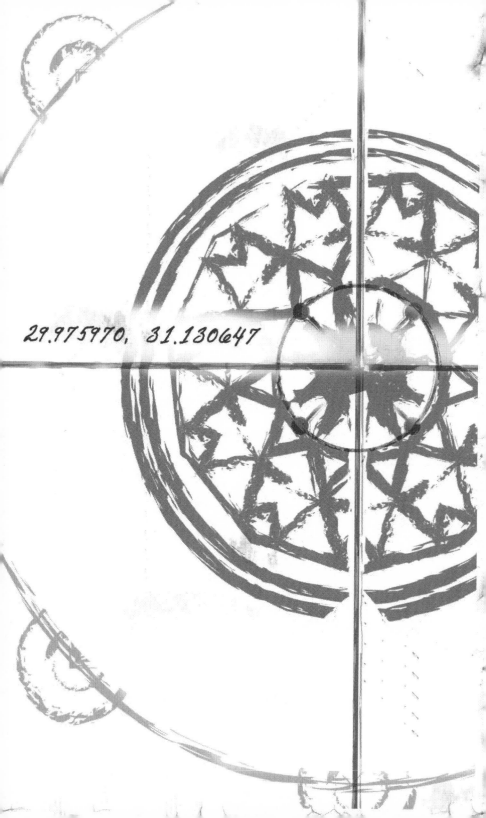

29.975970, 31.130647

4

Journal29.com/4

Scan or visit
the url above
to answer and
collect the key

key.4: _____

{key.1}

–

{key.2}

+

{key.3}

Journal29.com/5

Scan or visit
the url above
to answer and
collect the key

key.5: _____

a way in???

e

i   e   e   r   h   t   n

g   o   f   e   n   i   e

h   n   i   v   e   n   r

t   e   f   o   u   r   e

e   l   e   v   e   n   s

Journal29.com/6

Scan or visit
the url above
to answer and
collect the key

key.6: _____

something is wrong
inform team.

Journal29.com/7

 Scan or visit
the url above
to answer and
collect the key

key.7: _____

{key.6}x{key.5}xlead

Journal29.com/8

Scan or visit
the url above
to answer and
collect the key

key.8: _____

9

Journal29.com/9

Scan or visit
the url above
to answer and
collect the key

key.9: _____

33FRCDG

they were here before...

?

10

Journal29.com/10

Scan or visit
the url above
to answer and
collect the key

key.10: _____

that is the
{key.9} {key.8}

Journal29.com/11

Scan or visit
the url above
to answer and
collect the key

key.11: _____

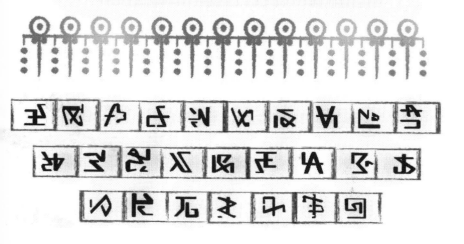

Journal29.com/12

Scan or visit
the url above
to answer and
collect the key

key.12: _____

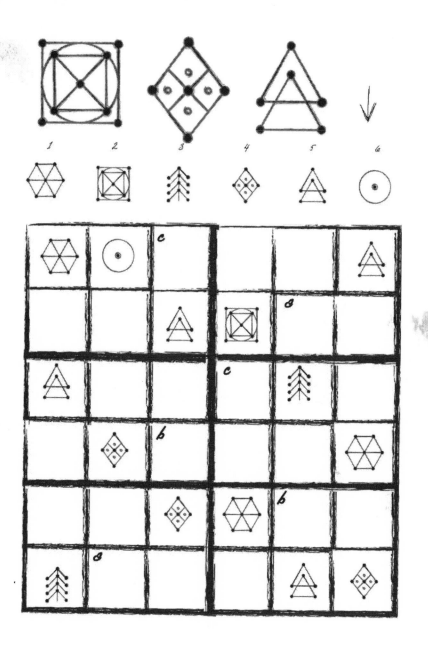

1   2   3   4   5   6

Ok let's count now

a.{key.4} b.{key.7} c.{key.10}

Journal29.com/13

Scan or visit
the url above
to answer and
collect the key

key.13: _____

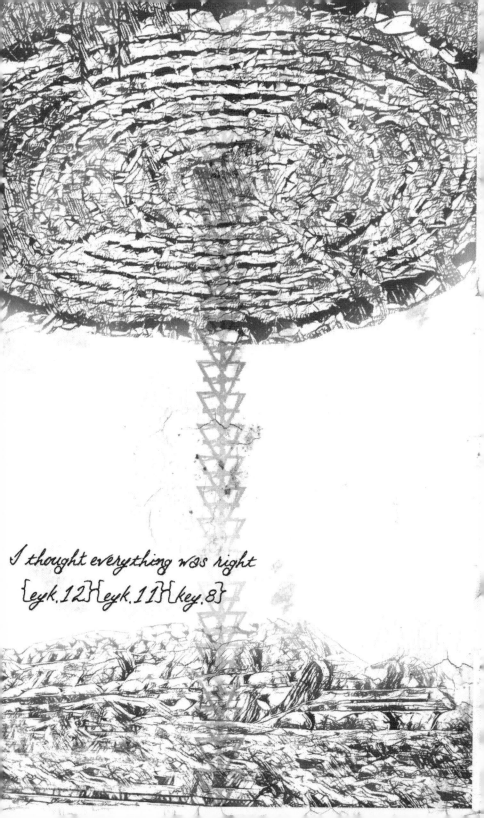

I thought everything was right
{eyk.12}{eyk.11}{key.8}

Journal29.com/14

Scan or visit
the url above
to answer and
collect the key

key.14: _____

It's too dark here... I can't see anything

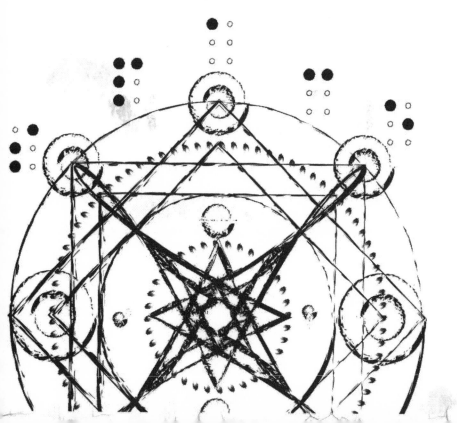

15

Journal29.com/15

Scan or visit
the url above
to answer and
collect the key

key.15: _____

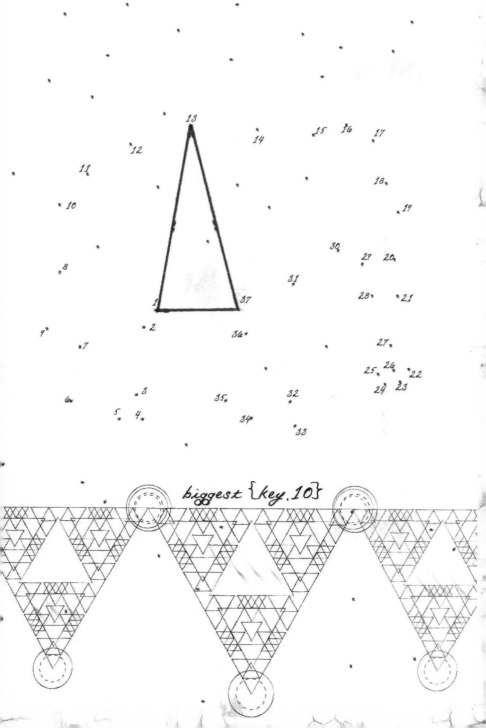

biggest {key.10}

16

Journal29.com/16

Scan or visit
the url above
to answer and
collect the key

key.16: _____

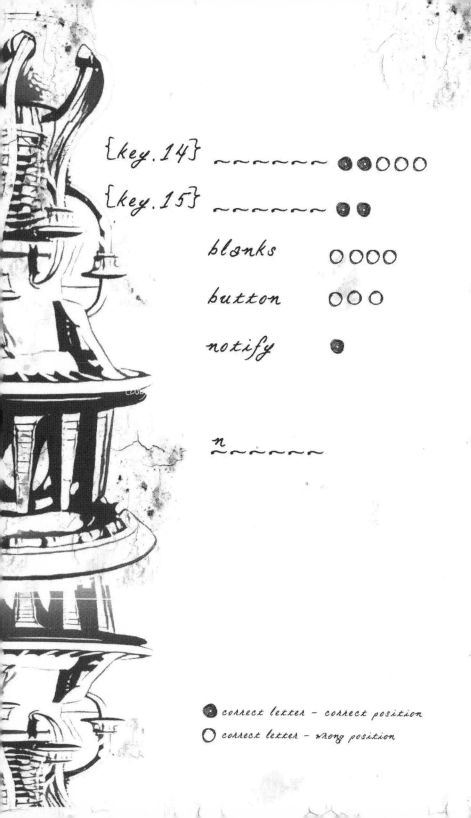

{key.14} ~~~~~~~ ●●○○○

{key.15} ~~~~~~~ ●●●

blanks ○○○○

button ○○○

notify ●

n ~~~~~~

● correct letter – correct position
○ correct letter – wrong position

Journal29.com/17

Scan or visit
the url above
to answer and
collect the key

key.17: _____

Journal29.com/18

Scan or visit
the url above
to answer and
collect the key

key.18: _____

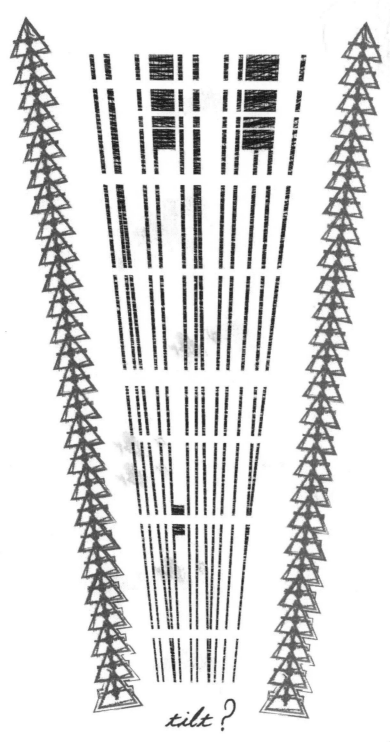

tilt ?

Journal29.com/19

 Scan or visit
the url above
to answer and
collect the key

key.19: _____

{key. 17}

17

-14

add them

{key. 18}

(20)

Journal29.com/20

Scan or visit
the url above
to answer and
collect the key

key.20: _____

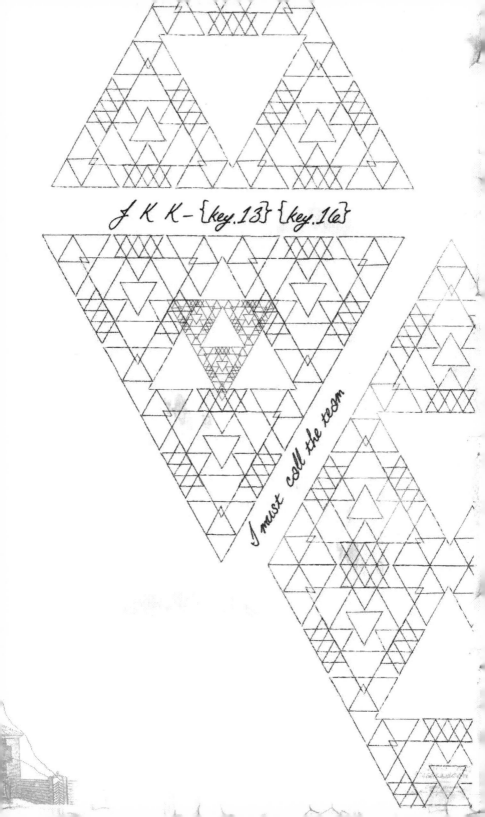

J K K - {key.13} {key.16}

I must call the team

21

Journal29.com/21

Scan or visit
the url above
to answer and
collect the key

key.21: _____

Now the hungry lion roars,
And the wolf behowls the moon,
Whilst the heavy ploughman snores,
All with weary task fordone.
Now the wasted brands do glow,
Whilst the screech-owl, screeching loud,
Puts the wretch that lies in woe
In remembrance of a shroud.
Now it is the time of night
That the graves all gaping wide,
Every one lets forth his sprite,
In the church-way paths to glide:
And we fairies, that do run
By the triple Hecate's team,
From the presence of the sun,
Following darkness like a dream,
Now are frolic: not a mouse
Shall disturb this hallow'd house:
I am sent with broom before,
To sweep the dust behind the door.

5-1-3 6-1-3 2-4-7 16-2-1 1-1-2 8-2-3

Journal29.com/22

Scan or visit
the url above
to answer and
collect the key

key.22: _____

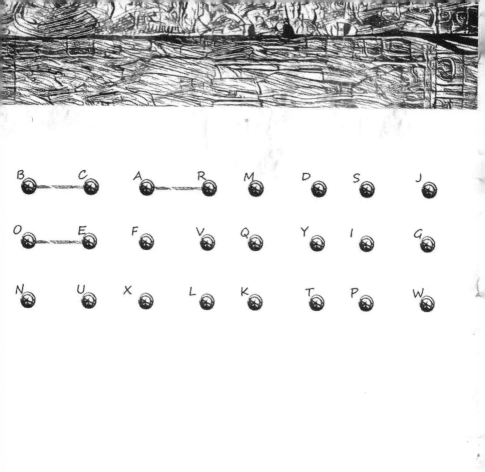

B—C   A—R   M   D   S   J

O—E   F   V   Q   Y   I   G

N   U   X   L   K   T   P   W

beam

cord

{key.20} ~~~~

{key.21} ~~~~

23

Journal29.com/23

Scan or visit
the url above
to answer and
collect the key

key 23: _____

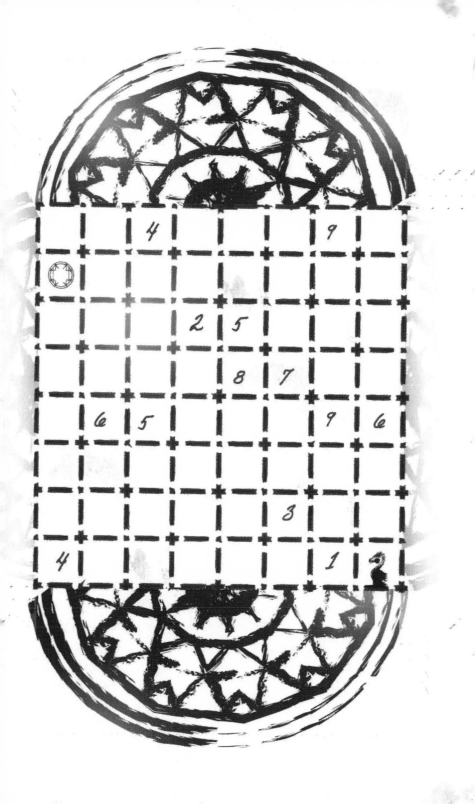

24

Journal29.com/24

Scan or visit
the url above
to answer and
collect the key

key.24: _____

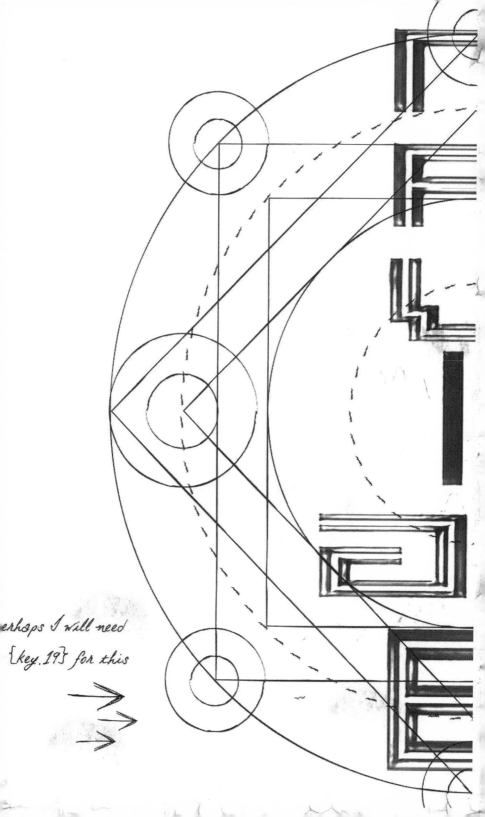

erhaps I will need
{key. 19} for this

Journal29.com/25

Scan or visit
the url above
to answer and
collect the key

key 25: _____

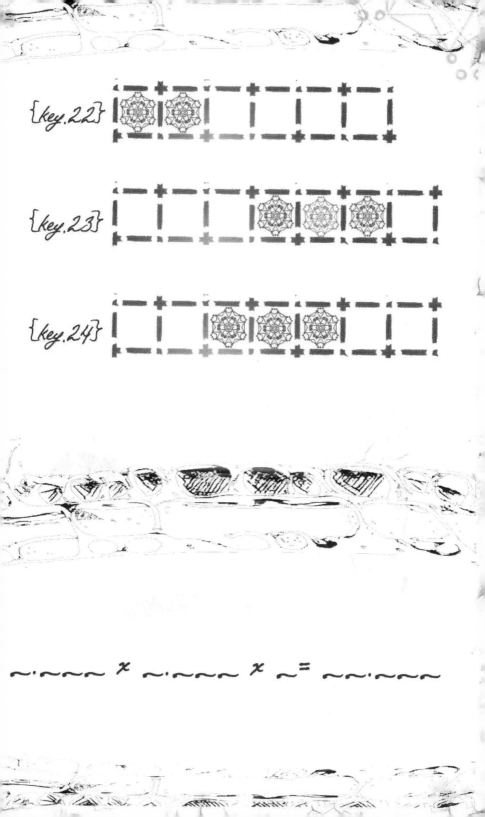

{key.22}

{key.23}

{key.24}

26

Journal29.com/26

Scan or visit
the url above
to answer and
collect the key

key.26: _____

(27)

Journal29.com/27

Scan or visit
the url above
to answer and
collect the key

key.27: _____

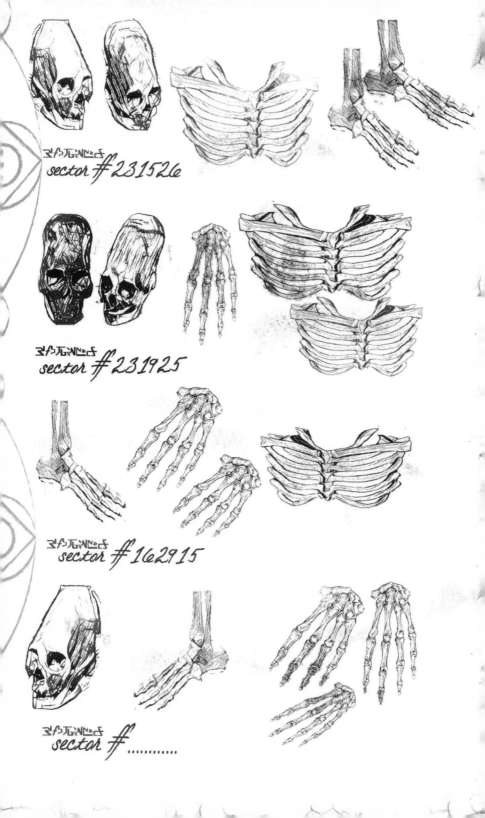

sector #231526

sector #231925

sector #162915

sector #...........

Journal29.com/28

Scan or visit
the url above
to answer and
collect the key

key.28: _____

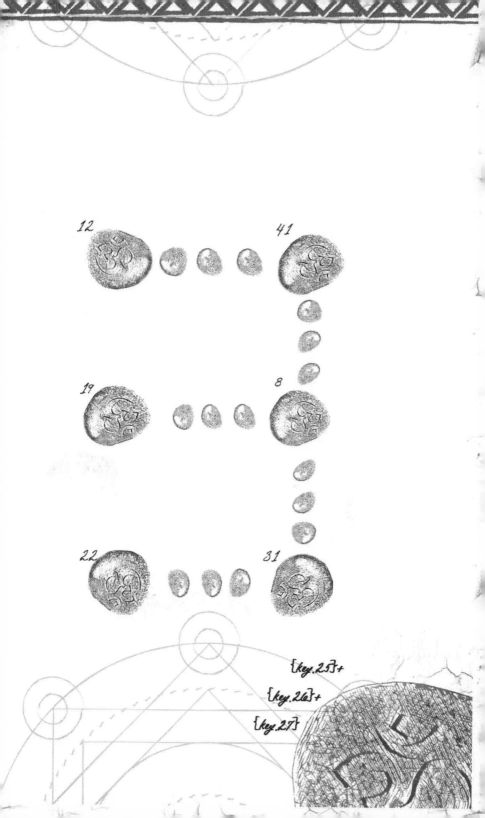

{key.25}+

{key.26a}+

{key.27}

29

Journal29.com/29

Scan or visit
the url above
to answer and
collect the key

key.29: _____

74

2

(b)

(c)

95

AxBxC

37

66

19

30

(a)

27

89

pencil ?

48

46

51

33

28

51

-1

94

12

94

61

28

08

12

36

45

85

54

45

33

39

29

78

61

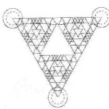

journal29.com/30

Scan or visit
the url above
to answer and
collect the key

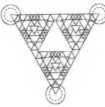

key.30: _____

Journal29.com/31

Scan or visit
the url above
to answer and
collect the key

key.31: _____

{key.28}

{key.29}

{key.30}

Journal29.com/32

Scan or visit
the url above
to answer and
collect the key

key.32: _____

Journal29.com/33

Scan or visit
the url above
to answer and
collect the key

key.33: _____

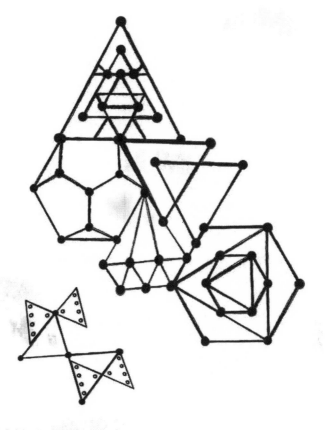

I have notes for this

34

Journal29.com/34

Scan or visit
the url above
to answer and
collect the key

key.34: _____

journal29.com/{key.32}{key.33}

35

journal29.com/35

 Scan or visit the url above to answer and collect the key

key.35: _____

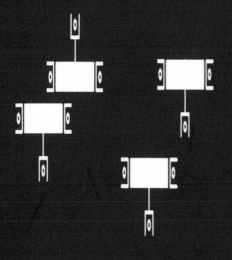

Journal29.com/36

Scan or visit
the url above
to answer and
collect the key

key.36: _____

remember
please this:
check the
{key.31}

Journal29.com/37

Scan or visit
the url above
to answer and
collect the key

key.37: _____

{Llave.34} {Clé.35} {Schlüssel.36}

journal29.com/38

Scan or visit
the url above
to answer and
collect the key

key.38: _____

Intresting symbol.
I think I saw that
again somewhere...

a check for this too

...too many pages...

this is a little different
from the above but there
is somewhere, I must
serach it...

I need this too.

39

journal29.com/39

Scan or visit
the url above
to answer and
collect the key

key.39: _____

40

Journal29.com/40

Scan or visit
the url above
to answer and
collect the key

key.40: _____

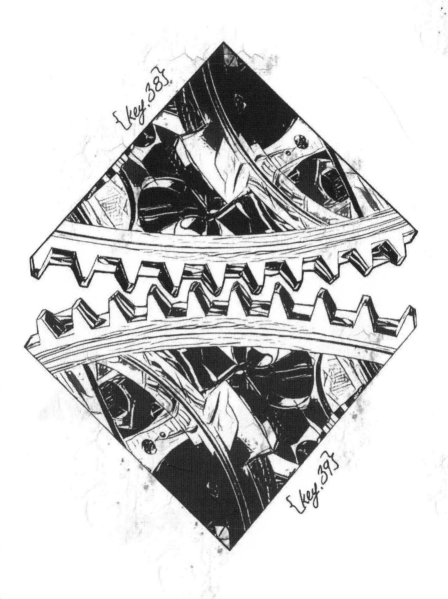

[key.38]

[key.39]

41

Journal29.com/41

Scan or visit
the url above
to answer and
collect the key

key.41: _____

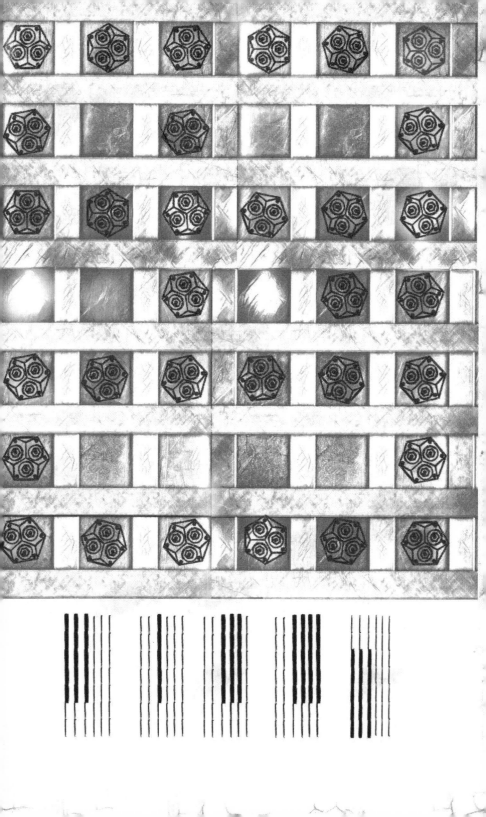

42

Journal29.com/42

Scan or visit
the url above
to answer and
collect the key

key.42: _____

I saw these characters before

08071974

21071969

25122016

01071976 _ _

10112017 _ _

Journal29.com/43

Scan or visit
the url above
to answer and
collect the key

key.43: _____

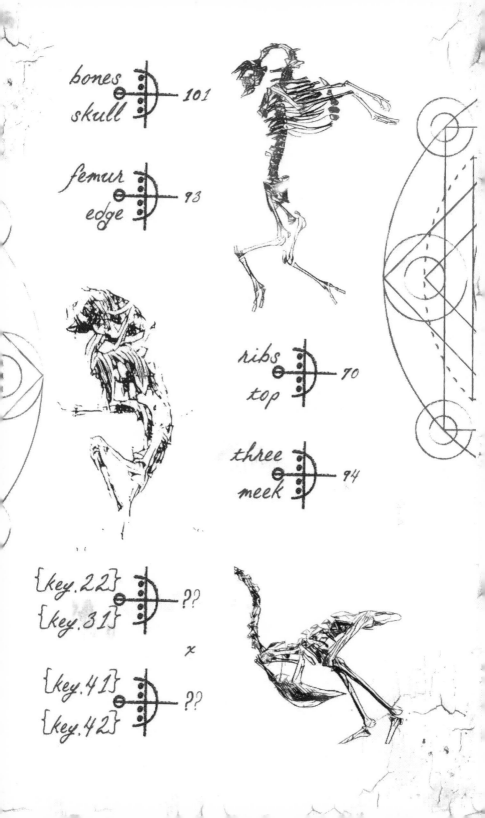

bones
skull — 101

femur
edge — 93

ribs
top — 70

three
meek — 94

{key.22}
{key.31} — ??

x

{key.41}
{key.42} — ??

Journal29.com/44

Scan or visit
the url above
to answer and
collect the key

key.44: _____

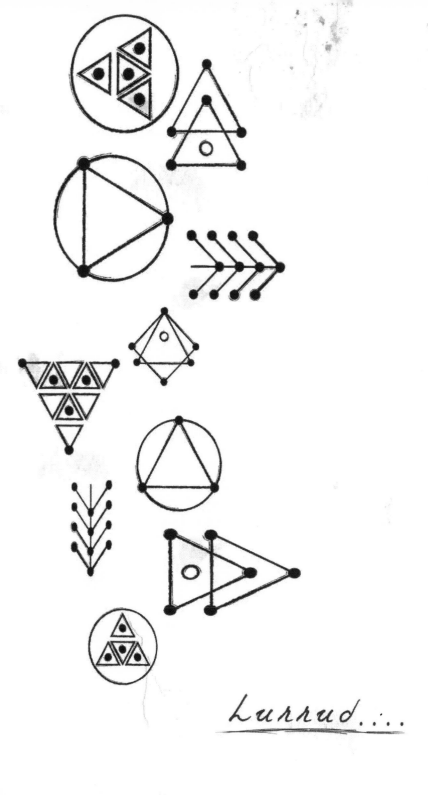

Lurrud....

Journal29.com/45

Scan or visit
the url above
to answer and
collect the key

key.45: _____

{key.40}{key.43}

1.

2.

28

49

62   14

3.

77

21

35   81

4.

1. x 2. x 3. x 4.

46

Journal29.com/46

Scan or visit
the url above
to answer and
collect the key

key.46: _____

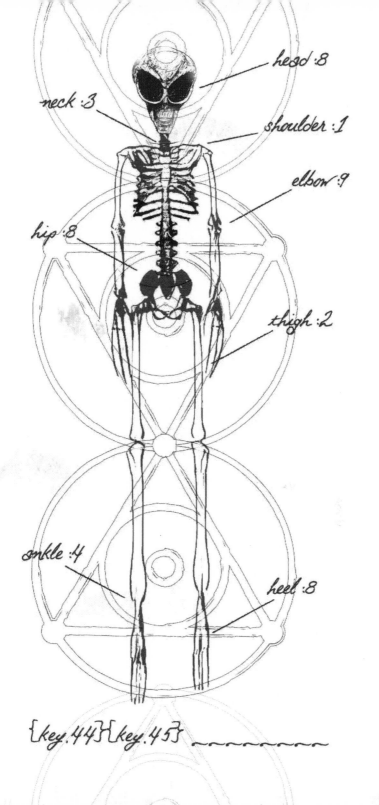

head :8

neck :3

shoulder :1

elbow :9

hip :8

thigh :2

ankle :4

heel :8

{key.44}{key.45}

Journal29.com/47

Scan or visit
the url above
to answer and
collect the key

key.47: _____

A D E V O I F M S N X

E
Z
R
C
S
B
L
O
A
G

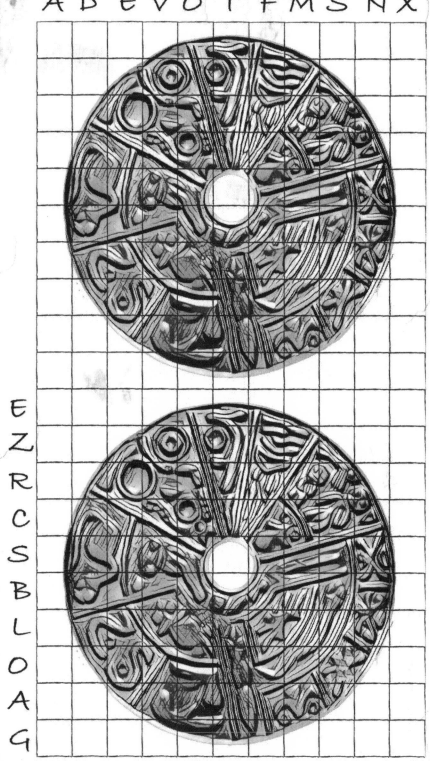

journal29.com/48

Scan or visit
the url above
to answer and
collect the key

key.48: _____

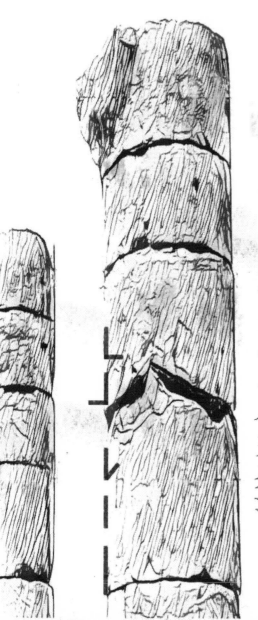

the indefinite continued progress of existence and events that occur in apparently irreversible succession from the past through the present to the future

journal29.com/49

Scan or visit
the url above
to answer and
collect the key

key.49: _____

3
9
5
1
8
4
1
2
1
5
8
6
5
0
8
8
7

{key.47}{key.48} ~~~~~

Journal29.com/50

Scan or visit
the url above
to answer and
collect the key

key.50: _____

slide and sum

journal29.com/51

Scan or visit
the url above
to answer and
collect the key

key. 51: _____

journal29.com/{Key.37}

Journal29.com/52

Scan or visit
the url above
to answer and
collect the key

key.52: _____

Night

Left

{Key.34}

{Key.50}

{Key.51}

Day

Right

Year

Journal29.com/53

Scan or visit
the url above
to answer and
collect the key

key.53: _____

1

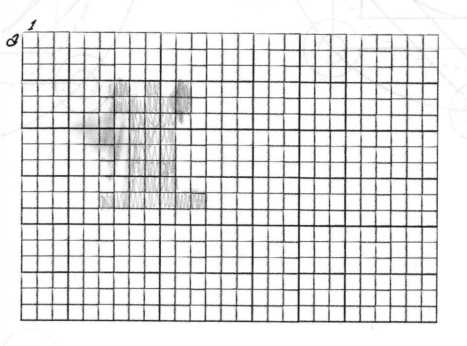

d7 d9 d11 e7 e8 e9 e10 e11 f8 f9 f10 i8 i9 i10

g8 g9 g10 j8 j9 j10 k6 k7 k8 k9 k10 k11 k12

h8 h9 h10   {Key.26} {Key.22} away

Journal29.com/54

Scan or visit
the url above
to answer and
collect the key

key.54: _____

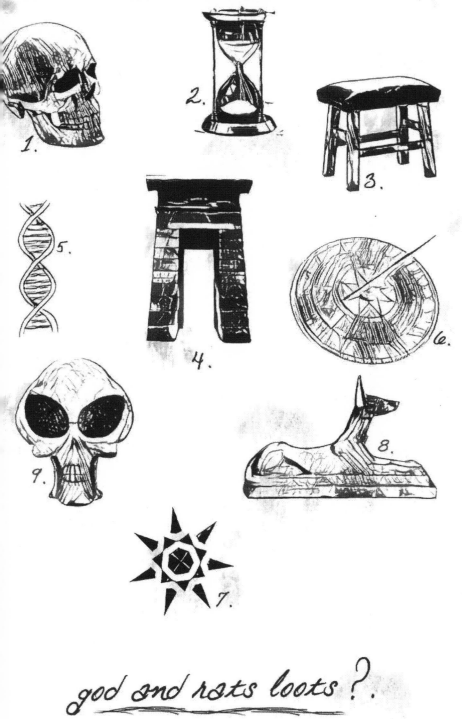

1. 2. 3. 5. 4. 6. 9. 8. 7.

god and rats loots ?.

Journal29.com/55

Scan or visit
the url above
to answer and
collect the key

key.55: _____

```
SPOT85WING26FIRE72
99LEFT13SEED58JAVA
43DOOR27NOVA36KING
81LIST97STER88ROOT
49EXIT94PEEK54MASK
ZEAL57ROAD63BOOT89
NONE36SOON81BEAM69
```

 no {Key.46} x

 great {Key.49} x

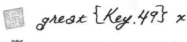 end of {Key.52} =

journal29.com/56

Scan or visit
the url above
to answer and
collect the key

key.56: _____

{key.53}+{key.49}-({key.55}{key.54})

journal29.com/57

Scan or visit
the url above
to answer and
collect the key

key 57: _____

up2
left1
up1
right0,5
down0,5
right0,5
up2
right0,5
down1
right0,5
up0,5
right0,5
down1
left1
down3

Journal29.com/58

Scan or visit
the url above
to answer and
collect the key

key.58: _____

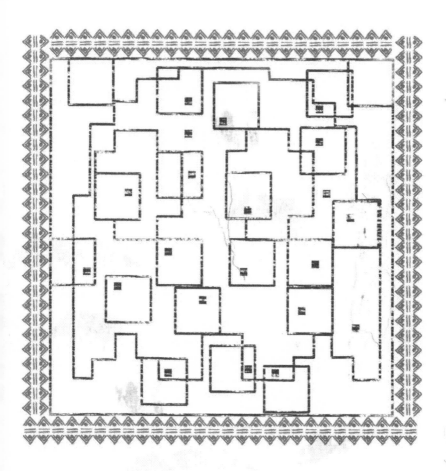

journal29.com/59

Scan or visit
the url above
to answer and
collect the key

key.59: _____

{Key.57} {Key.58}

extreme gravity
↓

journal29.com/60

Scan or visit
the url above
to answer and
collect the key

key.60: _____

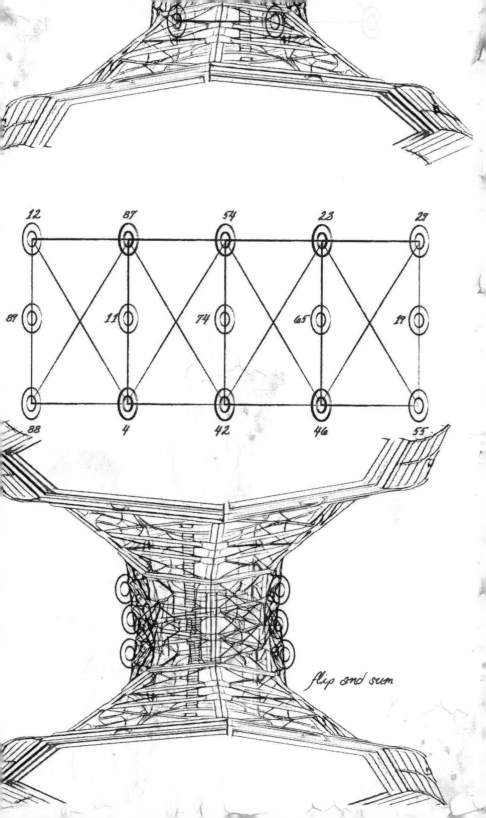

12 87 54 23 27

87 11 74 65 27

88 4 42 46 55

flip and sum

journal29.com/61

Scan or visit
the url above
to answer and
collect the key

key.61: _____

journal29.com/62

Scan or visit
the url above
to answer and
collect the key

key.62: _____

{Key.59} {Key.60}

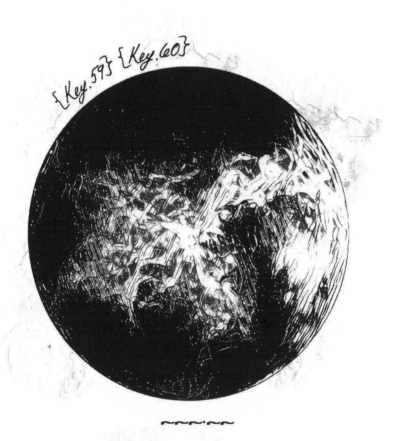

Journal29.com/63

Scan or visit
the url above
to answer and
collect the key

key.63: _____

The End?

{Key.61}{Key.62}{Key.59}{Key.60}

Notes

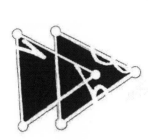

journal29.com/notes

Notes

Notes

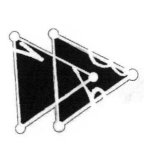

journal29.com/notes

CREDITS
SPECIAL THANKS TO ALL WHO MADE THIS BOOK A REALITY

SILVER CREDITS

ANDREW BROWN	FLO.BEG
LIU LIAN	GABOR SCHNEIDER
SANDYENGLAND	JOHN E GODARD
CLOAKED ONE	FRANKIE LEE
RICHARD REES	CLYDE CRAIG
PAOLO JAUCIAN	KRIANGKRAI WIKROMLERT
JOHN LESLIE	HUEN SU SAN
LAKE.KUBILIUS	ANGELIQUE J
BROOK ELGRABLY	BRENDA WOODS
MARIUSZ BIELEWICZ	ED ALLARD
CAVADENTI JULIAN	GARY EULENFELD
GEORGE ATTFIELD	TAMARA BERMUDES
CHARLES CLARK	NIKLAS DAHLMAN
KYLE WEATHERLY	MICHAEL WAREHAM
ADEN JACQUES	NANCI5
LIBBY SHARPE	WHATCHA MCCALLUM
BEN RUSSO	JEFF MCFADDEN
CONSTANTIN ERCKENBRECHT	ANNA HAJZMANOVA
AAHALL.RN	FRAN LOPES
PHIL RANTA	STEVEN PHILLIPS
DEVON VITKOVSKY	JOSEPH AU
BRETT REAY	KOHLROGGE
VIRGINIE KIDWELL	MARCUSAN1983
MELISSA DIXON	KOHLROGGE
CARTOON KID	STRGZR
BRUNO JESUS	PETER STAHLBERG
JOHN BOUDREAUX	ERIC SIROIS
GRANT FREER	EKGAM
ROBERT BEACH	ALAN PEACOCK
ALLAN OLSEN	TAYLOR DUNLAP
MICHAEL SIMPSON	WILLIAM.BATTLINE
LORNE MITCHELL	CANIDAE_OOKAMI
DAVE HUTCHINSON	MICHAEL THON
TYSON HAVERKORT	CANIDAE_OOKAMI
SASSAN VARASTEH	DRANDREDUMONT
MATTHIAS EVERTZ	ETHAN ZOHN
ALASSIETH	KIMBERLY NELSON
SAHARRIS	NEITHAN
NIKOS DAKOS	CLAIRE LEVERS

Silver Credits

Laura Innis
Smellylettuce
Laurie Mair
Chris.Ramirez1208
Charlotte Nachtegael
Linda Thomas
Panagiotis Karachalios
Simon Parkin
Rene Vendrig
Erica Palmer
Mikko Peltola
Patricia Alonso Calvo
Cdtindal8079
Yat Chung Ho
Jun Fukae
George Zwier
Jordan Tasker
Thomas Schwarzbraun
Christoph Brosius
Goichi55
Roy Simkes
Kseniia Oksenich
RJ Vanderwerf
John Rhoods
Phil Francis
Gijs Geers
Bernhard Henning
David Lecompte
Russ Hewson
Clinton Wong
BVK
Shane Stephens
Keith Force
Antti Vikman
Lindsey Wilkins
David Bowden
Panekattack
Madison Rhoades
Cova Donga

AJ Matunis
Andrew Preble
Philip Kirmser
Needbeef
Nicholas J. Corkigian
NRS66
Rene Ferris
Sebastian Sarbora
A.J. Biddles
Riley Farrar
Morinpm
Janelle Baril
Todd Auldridge
Naomi Okiddy
Monique Ramsey
Samantha Thompson
Lori Goutbeck
Labyrinth Escape Games, Portland, OR
Laura Green
Daniel Gomez
Josua Kärnbo
Ed Kopec
Dick Wisenbaker
Mike Bernett
Caleb Miller
Ittkyle
Thomas Kernan
Heather Hall
Ben Berbach
Alexandria Delarue
Lain Giraffe
Justin Pattelli
Matthew Hanley
Yabanjin
Gilles Pütz
Dylan Latimer
Jacob Kesler
Douglas Livingstone

SILVER CREDITS

KLAS MEDER BOQVIST	MANOS KOUFAKIS
MATT BAINBRIDGE	HELEN BOARDMAN
KEVIN MULVEY	CHARLIE
SPENCER THOMAS	GERASIMOS POLITIS
BOB RICHARDS	THOMASCJACKSON
JESSICA A LARUSCH	STEVE BISTLINE
DASHIEL MUNDING	CHANTAL LAWRENCE
RYAN THOMPSON	LEE CONAWAY
LAURA HANSFORD	PETER BOLHUIS
ADAM HUNTER	LEONIDAS LAZOPOULOS
JOAKIM NILSSON	ADRI AN
DAMIAN Z ESPARZA	TKYRIOS
ANTHONY.GRAND	VOLKER BACHE
CHRISTOPHER EWENS	BRIAN DAVIDSON
ZACKARY BRUCE	FILOTHEOS BEZERIANOS
SPAJ.KUF	DEAN O'DONNELL
SŁAWEK BIEL	NATHAN JONES
MATTHEW KARABACHE	AZIM ABASBEK
LIZ DIMITRIOU	VASILEIOS KARYMPALIS
JOSEPH MCCORMACK	ROBERT MCPHERSON
MCGUARD000-BIRD	SWANNEKKE
BILL TSELEPIS	FRANZISKA HECK
ALAN SMITH	NEIL ZUSSMAN
JIM CLARKE	CHRISTOPHER LIPPIATT
ELENA KOUFAKI	MARIOS MAVROUDIS
ALEX DRIGAN	SOPHIA QIN
VASILIKI MITRAKOS	PAVLOS CHRISOCHOIDIS
SATOSHI KIDA	VERONICA VENTURI
IOANNIS KOKOLAKIS	MICHAEL TASERUD
BEN MILAZZO	EMMA HALL
BRENDAN LUTZ	THERESA PIAZZA
THOMAS D KRAMER JR	DEREK HURLEY
JUSTYN KNUTSON	MARIA SOTIRI
KATARZYNA TORON	THOMAS GIBON
GUILLAUME DROULEZ	MARIA SAKKOU
AIKATERINI LYRONI	MARVIN SOETANTO
HOLGER DUBBEN	MATTHEW REES
LENNART NASCHKE	LEONARDO
MARKO CICAK	YOGI

SILVER CREDITS

Roberto Cano
Lachezar Blagoev
Skouras M. Panagiotis
Ole Sandbæk Jørgensen
Frederic Rodrigues
Arthur Duineveld
Mandy Sepers
Nikos Papastamopoulos
Ioanna Maria Nella
Zachari Dahran
Can Koklu
Aggeliki Katsika
Steen Limuel
Gordon Chan
Lucas Becsi Valiengo
Andrew Jarvis
Sarah Clauws
Jonathan Whitfield
Sarah Schulp
Arnaud Tournier
Adam Schulp
Chee Lup Wan
Andrea Monti
Vasilis Papaioannou
Nassia Vlachou
Efstathia Spanou
Jimmy Chim
Erhan Can İşeri
Bjorn Zock
Noelia y Amir
Chase Davis
Adrian Mueller
Michael Mcgee
Anelize Vendeth Scavassa
Ariel Polanco
Ioannis Lalopoulos
Jesper Albér Borré
Arianoglou Dimitris

Ioannou Hadjisoteriou
Kalamiotis Stamatis
Thanasainas Panagiotis
Alexandra Parau
Marwys
Valentijn Egbers
Sophia Arsinoi Papadimitriou
Gareth Wills
David Eisenhauer
Verna Fisher-Stokes
Reibab Rodacsep
Nadia Katsikerou
Thomas Roulin
Mikaela Mclean
Stephen Coombes
Ioannis Sclavos
Vasso Kalaitzidou
Giannoulis
Claire Levers
Annakowalewski
Antonia Papagianni
Kostas Kastanis
Brenda Woods
Ged Darko
Michael Dunlip
Chris Paight
Lizboulter
Marleen Hendrikse
Renaud Morineau
John Hadeed
Daniel Castello Garcia
Athanasios Arvanitidis
Michael Nauheimer
Mona Dozeman
Natasha Bennett
Geert-Jan Van Der Heide
Valent Cerovečki
Natasa Kelemeni

GOLDEN CREDITS

CHRISTIAN THILL
NORMA COLLICOTT
PAUL CLAPS
KELLY HOPPER
TETRAHEDRA.WORKS
BARBI BISHOP
ROB CRAIG
MAD CASEY
CURTUS FETTERS
ILIAS KOKKORIS
LESTER MARRISON
GADGET FLOW
IRENE MARGIOLAKI
ZISSIS BELLAS

CREATED BY
DIMITRIS CHASSAPAKIS